Try these at home!

Contains
SERIOUSLY SCIENCEY
experiments

WARNING: Some MESSY
stuff inside. Ask a grown-up

BY **JANE CLARKE** ILLUSTRATED BY **JAMES BROWN**

AL'S AWESOME SCIENCE

Busy Bodies!

FIVE QUILLS

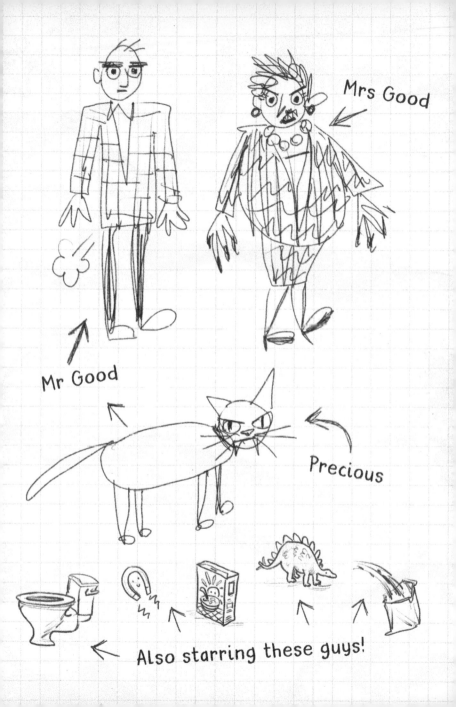

Mrs Good

Mr Good

Precious

Also starring these guys!

To Ruth, the best friend anyone could ever have – J.C.

For James, Lorraine, Austin and Iris x – J.B.

AL'S AWESOME SCIENCE: BUSY BODIES

First published in Great Britain in 2019 by Five Quills
93 Oakwood Court, London W14 8JZ

www.fivequills.co.uk

Five Quills is a trademark of Five Quills

Edited by Natascha Biebow at Blue Elephant Storyshaping
Designed by Becky Chilcott

A CIP record for this title is available from the British Library

ISBN 978 0 993553 76 9

1 3 5 7 9 10 8 6 4 2

Printed and bound in Great Britain by Clays Ltd, Elcograf S.p.A.

CONTENTS

In a Spin

Al Boffin stretched out his arms and started to spin around as fast as he could.

He was close to finishing his new experiment. How many spins could he do and still walk in a straight line?

He counted. "**ONE, TWO, THREE, FOUR ...**"

His dog, Einstein, gave an excited

WOOF! and began to chase his tail around in circles.

"... **FIVE, SIX ...** " Al stopped spinning. He tried to put one foot on the straight line he had chalked across the floor tiles to the back door. It was already very smudged.

"**WUURGH!**" he groaned.

He staggered into the fridge, dislodging a fridge magnet. His dental check-up reminder card fell to the floor and disappeared beneath it.

Einstein's legs skittered under him as he came to a halt.

Al sat on the floor until he felt less dizzy, then he brushed chalk off his shorts, took his notebook out of his pocket and recorded his results.

"What are you two up to?" Al's twin sister Lottie poked her head round the kitchen door, and elbowed her way in.

She was using both hands to

carefully carry a glass tumbler with a postcard balanced on the top of it.

"I think Einstein's been trying to catch his tail," Al told her, "but I'm experimenting to find out what happens if you step out of a time machine when it's been in a spin!"

Al glanced at the tumble drier. A stuffed stegosaurus was going round and round in it.

"Hey, what's Steggy doing in there?!" Lottie cried. She put down the glass tumbler and pulled the old toy out of the tumble drier. "He was a present from Dad. He's really precious."

"I know," Al said, seriously. Their dad had died when they were young so they both treasured things he'd given them. "I wanted to see him spin like he was in a time machine. I made sure the drier was on a slow speed and it wasn't too hot for Steggy."

Lottie carefully checked over her precious toy. She breathed a sigh of relief. "He's OK!"

"And stuffed toys don't feel dizzy at all." Al grinned. "Unlike me! I can't seem to walk in a straight line after I've spun around more than a couple of times . . ."

Lottie carefully placed Steggy on the high shelf next to the back door, where Einstein couldn't reach him.

"Your inner ears control your balance," Lottie explained. "They're making you dizzy."

"How?" Al asked.

"I can show you what's going on in your inner ear," Lottie said. She found a mug and half-filled it with water. She swirled the water round in the mug, then held it still. Al looked inside. The water was still swirling round.

"See? When you spin, the liquid inside your ear spins too. But the

liquid keeps swishing around even when you've stopped. Your brain gets confused because it's trying to work out whether you've stopped moving or not – and that makes you feel dizzy."

AWESOME FACT: THE INNER EAR

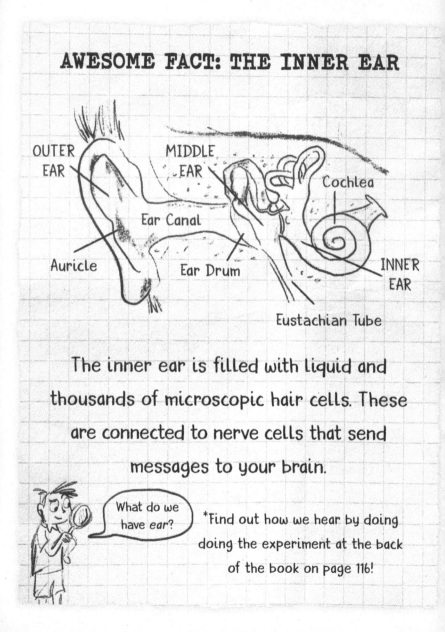

OUTER EAR

MIDDLE EAR

Cochlea

Ear Canal

Auricle

Ear Drum

INNER EAR

Eustachian Tube

The inner ear is filled with liquid and thousands of microscopic hair cells. These are connected to nerve cells that send messages to your brain.

What do we have *ear*?

*Find out how we hear by doing doing the experiment at the back of the book on page 116!

"I got dizzy just spinning in the kitchen," Al said. "It'll be worse if we're cooped up in a time machine in outer Space. I need to do some more experiments to find out what else might happen to your body if you travel through Space and time!"

AL'S IN A SPIN EXPERIMENT

(?) To find out how many spins you can do and still walk in a straight line. (?)

What Al used:

Himself

A large space

A piece of chalk

What Al did:

He drew a long line on the kitchen floor with the piece of chalk.*

*Al used chalk so it would rub off and not leave a mark!

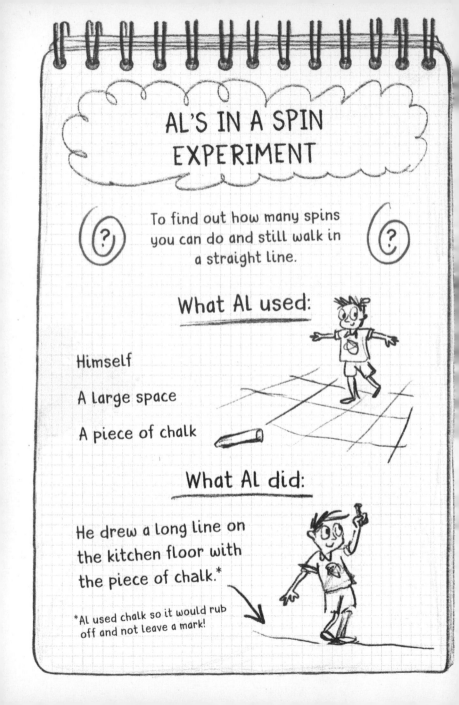

Al stood at the end of the line. He stretched out his arms and spun round once as fast as he could, then walked the line, putting his feet heel to toe.

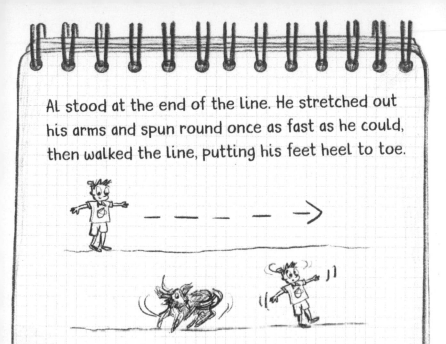

He repeated the experiment, doing an extra spin each time, and counted the number of straight-line steps.

Results:

NUMBER OF SPINS	NUMBER OF STEPS
1	10 (easy)
2	10 (slow and wobbly)
3	8
4	5
5	2
6	0 (wuuuuuurgh!)

Observations:

1. The more you spin, the dizzier you get, and the more difficult it is to walk in a straight line.

2. It might be better to do this outside where there's nothing to barge into.

3. Check with a grown-up before you draw a chalk line. Or use an imaginary line.

4. Try this with your friends and family. Everyone is different and will get different results.

Try it at home! What will you discover?
WARNING: ASK A GROWN-UP FIRST!
Make sure that you have plenty of space to
spin and won't hit anything or anyone!

"Shame the time machine has to be controlled by a human," Lottie said. "Time travel wouldn't bother insects. They experience the world in a different way from us." She grabbed the tumbler she'd put down and lifted the postcard off it. Nestled in the bottom was a great big earwig. "This one does, anyway!"

Al shuddered as he thought of a giant earwig at the controls of his time machine. He'd never shared Lottie's love of creepy crawlies.

Lottie put the postcard back on

the top and lifted up the tumbler so Al could see through it.

"Earwigs are awesome!" she told him. "They don't have ears, so they wouldn't get dizzy. They sense things around them with the hairs on their legs and on their antennae! You can see them if you look really closely, but it's better if you have a magnifying glass."

Al peered nervously at the pincers on the back end of the bug. "Don't they burrow into your ears and eat their way into your brain?"

"No," Lottie said indignantly. "The worst earwigs could do is give you a tiny pinch with their pincers, but that wouldn't be hard enough to hurt."

Al wasn't one hundred percent convinced.

"What are you going to do with it?" he asked.

"Let it go outside, of course. Earwigs like damp places. This one is quite fat so it might be a female who is expecting babies. They make really good mothers!" Lottie opened the back door and shook the earwig out into the rain. It scurried right back inside.

"**EEEK!**" Al shrieked as it ran over his foot, and scuttled under a gap in the skirting board. He hoped it was a male – he didn't like to think of baby earwigs making their home in the kitchen.

"Maybe it's a bit *too* damp outside today," Lottie commented.

Mum burst in from the shop, full of questions. "Who screamed? What happened? Are you all right?"

"Al saw an earwig," Lottie explained.

"Is that all?" Mum smiled tiredly. "I was worried that you'd hurt yourself." She ran her hand through her hair.

Mum seemed a bit stressed. She often was since Dad had died. That was why Al was doing all his experiments. He was hoping to invent a time machine so that he could take her back to a time when she was happier.

"Now, about this afternoon," Mum went on. "There's been a last-minute change of plan. I'm closing the shop because I have to go into town to see the accountant. But the sitter just called to let me know she's unwell and can't come round to keep an eye on you, so . . ."

Al and Lottie sighed with disappointment. They'd invited their friends Mia and Filip round, and now Mum was going to say that they would have to cancel and go with her to a boring old meeting . . . or was she?

"So I asked our neighbours if they'd

mind helping out, so I can see the accountant and concentrate on the advice she gives," Mum went on.

"The neighbours?" Lottie echoed. The twins looked at one another in alarm.

"After all the trouble you've caused them recently, I was ever so surprised when Mr and Mrs Good said yes," Mum added.

"The Goods are coming round?!" Al gasped as mental pictures of splattered eggs, floods, bottle rockets and an angry Mrs Good flashed through his brain.

"Yes," said Mum. "You'll be careful not to cause them any more trouble, won't you?"

Lottie nodded. "We'll try not to, won't we, Al?"

"I'm a scientist. Scientists are always careful!" said Al in a huff.

Feeling Queasy

Mum ushered Mr and Mrs Good into the living room. "It's such a pity it's raining so hard," she said apologetically. "I was hoping everyone could go outside to play this afternoon."

Lottie, Mia and Filip were standing in the middle of the room, taking it in turns to whirl around, while Al recorded their results. He closed his notebook

as the Goods came in. Mrs Good was
clutching her cat Precious. No wonder
he could hear barking!

"What have you done with Einstein?" Al asked Mum in a low voice.

"I shut him in the kitchen," Mum whispered. "Make sure he doesn't get out. You know what he's like if he sees Precious."

Al did know. Einstein was a gentle giant, but for some reason he couldn't stand the cat who lived next door.

Mum raised her voice so it could be heard above the barking. "Thank you so much, Mr and Mrs Good," she said. "While I'm out, kids, do something nice and quiet like colouring. I've put markers and paper out on the table. 'Bye!"

Al closed the door behind her. Einstein fell quiet.

In the living room, Mrs Good was busy introducing Precious to Al and Lottie's friends Mia and Filip.

"Precious doesn't like being left on her own inside the house," Mrs Good was saying. "You get bored on your own, don't you my sweetheart?"

Mr Good lowered himself down on a chair in the corner and opened his newspaper. "I expect there will be plenty to amuse her here," he said.

"Hello, Precious," said Filip, stretching out his hand. Precious tilted her ears to be scratched and began to purr.

"Precious doesn't normally let anyone but me touch her ears. She

likes you!" Mrs Good glanced round the room.

"Why have you pushed back the furniture?" she asked the twins, as she sat down and settled Precious on her lap.

"To make more room," Lottie explained. "We're doing some cool experiments that involve the inner ear and balance."

"Precious has very good balance," Mrs Good said proudly. "Have you seen the way she tightrope walks along the garden fence?"

Al nodded. It was probably best

not to add that he'd also seen the way that Precious' tightrope walk drove Einstein crazy.

"Our experiments are to do with dizziness," Filip told Mrs Good.

"We're counting how many spins we can do and still walk in a straight line," Mia added. "So far, I can do three, Filip, Lottie, and Al have only managed two!"

"Is that all? When I did ballet, I could do five pirouettes on one leg without getting dizzy," boasted Mrs Good, with a faraway look in her eyes.

Lottie, Filip and Mia stared at her

in amazement. Al's jaw nearly hit the ground as he pictured Mrs Good in a tutu.

"Ballet dancers and ice skaters are taught a technique called spotting to avoid dizziness," Mrs Good told them. "You concentrate your gaze on a fixed spot and follow it with your eyes until the last possible moment. Then you whip your head around and fixate on the spot again."

"We have to try that!" said Al.

The room erupted in giggles as Lottie, Al, Mia and Filip all attempted pirouettes. There was a loud **MEOW** as Al's outstretched arm swished over Precious' head. Precious jumped down from Mrs Good's lap.

"Stop spinning!" Mrs Good ordered.

"You're upsetting Precious!"

The four friends lay flat on the floor and tried to catch their breath. Al gazed up at the ceiling. It looked and felt as if the room was whirling round him.

He groaned. It made him feel nauseous. In a minute or two, the room had stopped moving and he was feeling better.

"That was odd," Lottie said. "It felt as if my brain was seeing things the wrong way."

"Yes, like when you're

sitting on a stopped train and you look out of the window and see another train moving and you feel as if you're moving," Mia added.

Filip sat up slowly. He was looking a bit green.

"Urgh!" he groaned. "I thought I was going to sick up my sandwiches."

"If you suffer from motion sickness, it's best to learn to pirouette on an empty stomach," Mrs Good told him.

Lottie agreed.

"That's right. If your stomach's full, and you throw up, that's a lot of vomit!"

"How much?" asked Al. His brain was working overtime. "Astronauts often suffer from motion sickness," he thought, "and the time machine will move through Space as well as time. We might need to take sick bags with us . . ."

"I'll show you," said Lottie. She disappeared into the kitchen and came back holding a see-through zip-up food bag, four slices of bread and a small glass of orange juice.

They all watched as she broke the bread up into small chunks, put it in the bag and poured in the orange juice.

"Imagine this bag is your stomach, Filip." Lottie giggled as she held the bag upright and squished up the contents until they went mushy.

Lottie carefully closed the bag and held it up so everyone could see the orange gloop inside. Mr and Mrs Good stared at it.

Al thought they looked a bit nervous. "Those really are mangled molecules!" he grinned. He took out his notebook and wrote **PACK LARGE SICK BAGS IN TIME MACHINE!**

"Your stomach churns up your food, and begins to digest it," Lottie went on. "When you throw up, your muscles contract and force the contents of your tummy out of your mouth!"

"What makes real sick smell so disgusting?" Al asked.

"It's the acid in our tummies that mixes with the food," Lottie said. "If I leave the bag to rest in the kitchen, the acid in the orange juice will make the bread go all smelly. Then the bag will fill with gas just like your tummy. If you squish it hard enough it will pop!"

"So why don't people go pop?" asked Mia.

"Because people burp and fart . . ." answered Lottie.

Mrs Good gasped. "You shouldn't use those words in polite company!"

"Sorry!" Lottie giggled. "I meant to say that people don't pop when their tummies are full of gas because they . . . erm . . . pass wind from both ends." She carried the bag of bread and orange juice into the kitchen and put it up on the shelf next to Steggy, out of Einstein's reach.

When Lottie came back into the living room, Mrs Good had a stern look on her face.

"Harold and I think that's quite enough about stomachs and digestion," she said. "But we know how much you love science. Are there any nice, clean experiments you can do?"

Al sighed. Travelling in a time machine was going to have all sorts of effects on the human body and there were loads more experiments he wanted to do about that, but it was hard to think of one that was not messy and suitable for Mr and Mrs Good!

"I know one!" said Mia. "It shows that you can't always trust your eyes."

"Good idea!" Al grinned. Once he

was in a time machine, his brain was likely to get confused. It would be important to know how far he could trust senses like eyesight.

"We can do it at the table," Mia said, leading the way. The four friends sat down. Al was suddenly aware of Mrs Good looking over his shoulder.

"Can I join in?" she asked.

"Er . . . umm . . . yes, I suppose so!" Al spluttered in surprise.

LOTTIE'S TUMMY EXPERIMENT

To show how your stomach begins to digest food – and how it might throw it back up!

What Lottie used:

A one-litre zip-up plastic food bag

4 slices of bread

Half a glass of orange juice

What Lottie did:

She broke up the bread into smaller pieces and put them into the bag.

She poured in the orange juice.

She carefully held the top of the bag closed with one hand, and squashed and squeezed the contents with her other hand.

Then she closed the top of the bag, and left it to rest.

ZZZZZZZ

Results:

The squished-up bread and orange juice formed a mushy sludge.

When the bag was left to rest, gasses began to build up and the bag started to inflate.

I feel gassy!

Observations:

1. The acid in the orange juice gradually turns the bread into mush.

2. This is like the digestive process – stomach acid breaks down your food so your body can use its nutrients.

3. The digestive process is smelly.

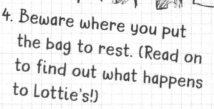

4. Beware where you put the bag to rest. (Read on to find out what happens to Lottie's!)

5. If you squeeze the bag hard enough the seal will give way and the contents will pop out – like how your abdominal muscles squeeze and make vomit shoot out of your mouth when you're sick.

Try it at home! What will you discover?
WARNING: ASK A GROWN-UP FIRST!
This experiment could get messy so make sure you do it outside or in the sink.

Blind Spot

"So what are you up to?" Mrs Good asked, pulling up a chair.

"It's an eyesight experiment," Al told her.

"Why do you need to experiment on eyes?" asked Mrs Good.

"Because . . . er, because . . ." Al paused. He couldn't tell Mrs Good that he wanted to know how far he could trust his eyes when he travelled in a time machine. She might tell Mum — and that would ruin the surprise!

". . . because our eyeballs are awesome!" he finally replied.

OUR AWESOME EYEBALL

Cool!

Your eyes work a bit like a camera!

When you look at something, the LENS of your eye focusses light on the RETINA at the back of your eye.

Special ROD AND CONE CELLS turn images into ELECTRICAL MESSAGES that are sent to the OPTIC NERVE. The optic nerve carries messages to the BRAIN, which tells you what you are seeing!

Image $\longrightarrow$ Eye $\longrightarrow$ Image $\longrightarrow$ Brain

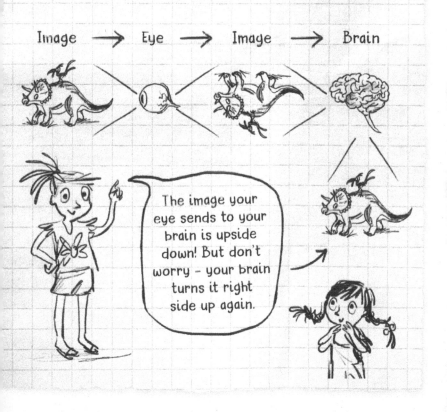

The image your eye sends to your brain is upside down! But don't worry - your brain turns it right side up again.

"I agree, eyeballs are er . . . super!"
Mrs Good said enthusiastically.

The twins looked at each other in surprise. They were used to Mrs Good being cross and scary. It was weird to hear Mrs Good be so enthusiastic.

"So you really want to do Mia's experiment?" Lottie asked in amazement.

"I do! That is, if it isn't messy. You know how I hate mess." Mrs Good took a mirror from her handbag and checked her hair and make-up were neat and tidy.

"This experiment isn't messy at all," Mia reassured her. She took a blank postcard and made a couple of marks on it with a black marker. "It's an experiment to prove you have a blind spot."

"Wow," thought Al, "if we all have

a blind spot, I'll need to make sure I don't miss anything when I'm in my time machine."

"I'm very observant!" exclaimed Mrs Good as Mia handed her the postcard.

"You are," agreed Lottie, ruefully.

The postcard had a dot on the left side and a small cross on the right side.

"Hold this out in front of you please, Mrs Good," Mia instructed. "Now, close one of your eyes and stare at the cross with the other eye as you bring the card towards your face."

They watched as Mrs Good slowly moved the card.

"Oooh!" Mrs Good exclaimed. "The dot disappeared." She moved the card closer to her nose. "It reappeared!" she squeaked.

"You found your blind spot!" Mia told Mrs Good. "Don't worry. All human beings have one."

"Harold, come and try this!" Mrs Good called to her husband.

"Coming, Mildred!" Mr Good hurried over and Mia repeated the blind spot experiment with him while Al wrote in his notebook.

"That really is very interesting," said Mr Good. His eyes twinkled with curiosity. "You do a lot of scientific experiments, don't you? Do they have any specific purpose?"

"Al's working on a . . ." Filip began.

Al silenced him with a look.

"A project for school," Al said, thinking quickly. "A science project."

"What's it about?" asked Mr Good.

"The Moon landings," said Al, who really was intending to do a project on them . . . sometime.

"I see!" said Mr Good with a huge grin. "It all makes sense now . . . the rocket that went down our chimney, the eggs that dropped into our garden, the bucket of water . . . those were all experiments to do with launching a spacecraft and landing it. Then today, the spinning and the stomach experiment were to see the effects on the body of Space travel . . . and the eye experiments are about whether or not you can trust what you see when you're in Space . . . "

Al breathed a sigh of relief. Mr Good had tied it all together nicely, but had got it a bit wrong. He clearly had no idea that the experiments had anything to do with inventing a time machine!

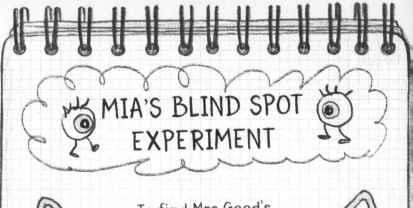

MIA'S BLIND SPOT EXPERIMENT

? To find Mrs Good's blind spot (or anyone else's, including your own). **?**

What Mia used:

A blank postcard or small piece of paper

A black marker

Mrs Good (or anyone else including you)

What Mia did:

With the marker, she drew a small dot on the left side of the postcard and a small cross on the right side.

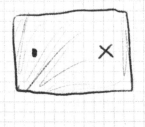

She told Mrs Good to hold the card at arm's length in front of her, close one eye and stare at the cross with the other, then slowly move the card closer to her face.

Results:

At a certain distance, the dot disappeared from Mrs Good's sight. Then it reappeared again. Mia found Mrs Good's blind spot.

Observations:

1. The blind spot is the area on the retina where the optic nerve connects the eye to the brain. This area has no rod or cone cells that respond to light, so an image that falls here can't be seen.

2. Lottie would like you to know that, unlike Mrs Good, an octopus does not have a blind spot!

3. People driving cars and lorries - and spaceships - have blind spots too! Never assume they can see you!

Try it at home! What will you discover?
WARNING: THIS EXPERIMENT
IS <u>NOT</u> MESSY!

LOTTIE'S FUN FACTS ABOUT ANIMAL EYES

Chameleons can look in two directions at once.

Tigers' night vision is around six times better than humans'.

Birds can see colours on wavelengths that are invisible to humans. For example, they see power lines as bursting with colours. These wavelengths are called ultraviolet.

Al thinks it would be great if Mrs Good had a really big blind spot when it came to spotting trouble.

Space Capsule

"I remember the Apollo missions to the Moon!" Mr Good's eyes shone. "I used to rush back from school every day

and switch on our black and white TV so I could watch the astronauts floating round in Space in zero gravity. They lived in very cramped conditions!"

"Imagine what it was like being so squashed up . . ." Al turned to Mr and Mrs Good. "Thanks for doing the eyesight experiment. It's still too wet to go outside, so I think we'll all go and . . . um . . . play upstairs for a while and give you both a break."

Mr and Mrs Good nodded as Mia, Filip and Lottie followed Al upstairs into Mum's bedroom. He opened the door to Mum's built-in wardrobe.

WARNING:

Only squish yourself into <u>BUILT-IN</u> wardrobes or cupboards. Climbing into a piece of freestanding furniture is a safety risk because it might fall on you! Also don't climb into wall cupboards. You might be too heavy for them and they might fall off the wall!

"Let's see what it's like to be squished into the capsule of a time machine!" Al said, pushing aside the hanging clothes and sitting down on a row of shoes. The others squashed in after him. Al was just about to close the door when there was a loud **MEOW**.

"Precious!" Lottie giggled as the cat crept into the wardrobe, clambered over their knees, and curled up in a corner next to Filip. "Does your Mumsie know you followed us up here?"

"Mrs Good would be in here with us if she knew!" Al shut the door, and it all went dark.

"Hey, someone just stuck their elbow in my ear," Mia complained.

"Sorry," muttered Filip. "I'm stroking Precious."

Precious' purrs rumbled round the wardrobe.

"We just about fit in," said Lottie. "But I wouldn't want to spend much time in such a small space, especially if everything's floating around in zero gravity. A time machine journey should be quick, shouldn't it?"

"When it works. But what if the time machine doesn't arrive instantly at the right place or time?" Al said worriedly. "We might have to make stops along the way. Then we'd have to live in the capsule for a while."

"You could train for it," Filip suggested. "Astronauts are trained to live in cramped conditions."

"Not as small as this," Mia said. "The International Space Station is about the size of a football pitch. It orbits the Earth in around 90 minutes so the astronauts get to see the sun rising and setting 15 or 16 times in a day."

"I want to be an astronaut," Mia said. "Maybe one day, I'll work on the International Space Station, or go on a mission to Mars!"

"Cool!" said Al. His tummy rumbled, making him think of food. "What are astronauts' meals like?"

"They eat all sorts of freeze-dried meals," said Mia. "And they do experiments on growing food in Space. That'll be important if there's ever a mission to Mars. They need to make sure the astronauts have a good diet, with lots of nutritional supplements, so they can keep healthy."

CRUMMY WARNING:

The International Space Station is a virtually weightless environment – there is no gravity in Space! Foods that make crumbs aren't allowed in case bits float off around the cabin and get stuck in the equipment. If you go there, there, you can't take biscuits, crisps or breakfast cereal!

"You'd better pack some food in your time machine," Lottie said. "I'd take chocolate bars with me, how about you, Filip?"

"Gherkins!" said Filip.

"Chocolate and gherkins are not a balanced diet!" Mia groaned.

Al was thinking. "Chocolate might melt and jars of pickles would be very heavy and might break. I need something easier to pack. Shame we can't take breakfast cereal. They put vitamins and iron in that!"

"Iron?" Filip sounded puzzled. "Iron is found in rocks!"

"Yep!" said Al. "And they put it in our breakfast cereal. I can show you with an experiment. Come on!"

Crunch Time

The four friends clattered down the stairs and burst into the kitchen. Einstein greeted them as if he hadn't seen them for years.

"It's okay, Einstein," Lottie said, pushing the dog away as he put his paws on her shoulders and covered her ear with loving licks. "There's no need to be jealous of a **C-A-T**."

Einstein's ears pricked up. He dropped on all four paws and slowly circled each of them, sniffing suspiciously at their clothes.

"He can smell the **C-A-T**," Lottie said. "Dogs' noses are much more sensitive than humans' noses."

Einstein gave them a reproachful look, then he sighed deeply and slunk off to his bed in the corner.

"He knows the spelling of **C-A-T** too," Filip laughed. "Maybe you were right to give him the name of a genius!"

Al got busy gathering the equipment he needed for the experiment. "Paper, plastic bag, cup, breadboard, rolling pin," he muttered as he rummaged through the drawers. "And a magnet. I remember seeing one in Great Grandpa Boffin's things. It's shaped like a horseshoe." He rushed upstairs to get it.

Al clattered back into the kitchen, then took a box of corn flakes out of the cupboard. Einstein looked up and started to whine.

"What's wrong with him?" Mia asked.

"He's just upset about Precious being in his house," Lottie explained. "Plus, he loves corn flakes. When he hears the box rattling he starts woofing and begging."

"It's not going to be easy to do this experiment with Einstein in the room," agreed Al. "Especially as I need to do some corn flake bashing and he's going to want to eat some . . ."

"It's too wet to put him outside," said Lottie. "Let's leave him in the kitchen and take the stuff through to the living room."

LOTTIE'S AWESOME FACT: PAVLOV'S DOGS

Ivan Pavlov, born 1849, was a Russian psychologist. He gave his dogs food after making a certain noise, like ringing a bell.

After a short time, the dogs began to drool when they heard the noise.

Psychologists call this a conditioned response. Einstein has one when he hears the box of corn flakes rattling.

Yum!

"So, what is your experiment about this time?" Mr Good asked, as Al put the breadboard and the rest of the things on the living room table. "Astronaut food?"

"You got it!" said Lottie, raising her voice above the dog whining that was coming through the kitchen door.

"Astronauts' bodies need iron and Al says he can prove there really is iron in corn flakes," Mia explained.

"It's not just astronauts," Mrs Good commented. "We all need iron in our blood. If you have too little, you can get sick. There's lots of iron in spinach, so I make Mr Good eat a lot of that."

"She does," Mr Good muttered grumpily.

They watched Al scoop a couple of cups of cereal into the plastic bag.

He squeezed out the air and closed it carefully. Then he put it down on the breadboard and grabbed the rolling pin. "Now for the fun bit!" he grinned.

In no time at all he'd bashed and rolled the cereal into a powder.

"Now watch, this!" Al opened the bag and tipped a little pile out onto a piece of white paper.

"Iron is magnetic, so it will stick to this," Al explained, pushing the magnet into the dusty heap.

"Ta-da!" he announced as he pulled the magnet out.

Sure enough, there were tiny pieces of cereal stuck to the magnet.

AL'S CEREAL EXPERIMENT

To detect the iron in fortified breakfast cereal.

What AL used:

2 cups of corn flakes (or another iron-fortified breakfast cereal*)

A plastic bag

A breadboard (or use any hard surface, like the floor)

A rolling pin (use the back of a spoon if you don't have a rolling pin)

A piece of white paper

A large magnet

*Look in the cereal packet's ingredients to find out if iron has been added.

What Al did:

He poured the two cups of corn flakes into the plastic bag.

He squashed the air out of the bag and made sure it was tightly closed.

He put the bag on a hard surface (the breadboard) and used the rolling pin to crush the cereal into a powder.

He tipped a small heap of powdered cereal on to the white paper.

He put the magnet into the powder and pulled it out.

Results:

Powdered corn flakes stuck to the magnet.

They stuck to the magnet because they contained iron, which is magnetic.

Observations:

1. Fortified breakfast cereals contain tiny pieces of iron.

2. If they contained big pieces, you might break your teeth on them.

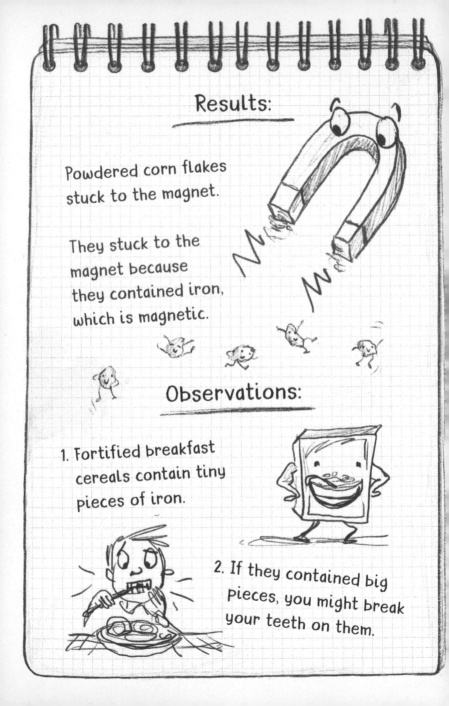

3. Don't bash so hard you break the plastic bag.

4. Dogs like crushed cereal – but so do birds, so put the powder outside for them to eat.

What does Einstein think Precious eats for breakfast?

Cereal-ously?

Mice Krispies!

Try it at home! What will you discover?
WARNING: ASK A GROWN-UP FIRST!
Try this experiment in the kitchen or outside where it is easy to clean up the crumbs!

"Mildred, dear, if breakfast cereal has plenty of iron in it, can I eat more cereal and less spinach?" Mr Good brought his face closer to the paper so he could peer shortsightedly at the magnet.

"A . . . A . . . A . . . TCHOO!" Mr Good sneezed loudly, blowing cereal dust all over the table. "Harold!" Mrs Good exclaimed. "Stop that at once. You're making a mess."

A series of thuds came from the kitchen. Einstein barked.

"YOUR DOG'S TRYING TO BREAK THROUGH THE DOOR TO GET AT MY PUSSYCAT!" Mrs Good shrieked.

"I don't think he is," Al said. "He's throwing himself at the back door, not this one."

"Uh-oh!" Lottie gave a little gasp. "When did he last go out?"

"This morning!" Al jumped up, hitting the box of breakfast cereal with the back of his hand.

The cereal box arced into the air and a shower of corn flakes rained down on Mr and Mrs Good's heads.

Busy Bodies

Einstein was standing by the back door. His ears and tail were drooping. Behind him, a big yellow puddle of doggy pee

was spreading over the kitchen floor.

Al rushed to the door. "It's OK, Einstein! It's not your fault. We should have remembered to let you out."

Al threw open the back door and Einstein shot out into the rain.

The door walloped the shelf where Lottie had put her old toy and the plastic stomach-bag, making them catapult into the air.

"**STEGGIE!**" Lottie gasped.

Al made a dive and caught his sister's precious toy before it hit the ground. But the bag landed on the floor and burst with a squelchy . . .

Smelly orange gloop exploded over Al's shoes and spattered across the floor.

"Maybe we can clean up this mess before anyone notices," Al said hopefully. He handed Steggie to Lottie and grabbed Mum's clean tea towel to wipe off his shoes.

But before anyone could do anything about the kitchen floor, Mrs Good hollered, "**CHILDREN!** Get in here and clean up these corn flakes!"

Al, Lottie, Mia and Filip slowly sidled into the living room.

Mr Good was combing corn flakes out of his hair. There was a faint **MEOW** from upstairs.

"**PRECIOUS!**" Mrs Good glanced wildly round the room. "**WHERE IS SHE?**" she asked ominously.

Her friendly face had disappeared. **"WHAT HAVE YOU DONE WITH HER?"**

"We didn't do anything with Precious," Al said indignantly. "She followed us into Mum's bedroom."

"She's fine," Filip reassured Mrs Good. "She's snuggled up in Mrs Boffin's wardrobe." There was another muffled **MEOW**.

"She must have got herself shut in!" Mrs Good leapt to her feet and made for the door. She thundered upstairs.

Al, Lottie, Mia, Filip and Mr Good raced after her.

"Mumsie's here, Precious!"
Mrs Good cried.

The four friends looked on as she dived head-first into the wardrobe and started to toss out the contents behind her.

"We'll have to tidy that up before Mum gets back," Lottie said, as the heap of clothes and shoes grew bigger and bigger.

Al nodded. The last thing they wanted to do was upset Mum.

"If you had a time machine," Filip whispered, "you could set it to go back to when we were doing the blind spot experiment. It was all going very well then!"

Mrs Good's head emerged from the empty wardrobe. Her hair was all messed up and her face was bright red.

"Precious isn't in there!" Mrs Good pointed a shaking finger at the twins. "This is all your fault. My poor pussycat. Where can she be?"

"Maybe she squeezed into a drawer?" Mia suggested.

Mum's underwear flew round the bedroom as Mrs Good frantically pulled open drawers and rifled through them.

MEEOW!

A loud kitty wail came from the bathroom.

"PRECIOUS! HOLD ON! MUMSIE'S COMING!" Mrs Good cried. She threw open the bathroom door and she screamed.

'NOOOOO OOOO!"

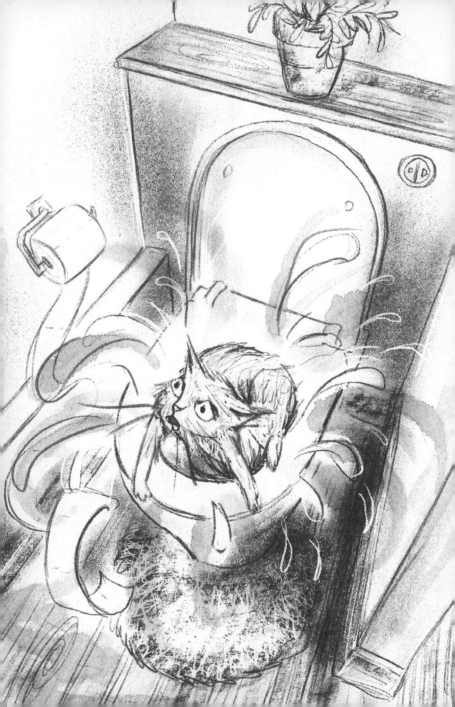

Everyone crammed in the doorway to take a look. Precious was in the toilet bowl. Her front paws were on the toilet seat and she was scrabbling frantically to get out. Her ears were wet and bedraggled.

"She must have gone for a drink and slipped in," Lottie whispered.

"HAROLD, DO SOMETHING!"

Mrs Good shrieked.

Mr Good reluctantly reached down and pulled out the dripping wet cat.

"She's drenched," he muttered, holding Precious at arm's length.

Al handed him one of Mum's best bath towels. Mr Good wrapped the wriggly cat in the towel and handed her over to his wife.

"**PRECIOUS!** Don't worry. Mumsie's got you. You're safe now!" Mrs Good crooned as she cradled her pet in her arms and carried her downstairs. "Let's put you into the kitchen sink and get that nasty lavatory water off you."

Precious thrashed her tail, splashing toilet water over the stair carpet and the landing wall as Mrs Good headed for the kitchen.

"Make sure Einstein's not in there," Lottie warned from the top of the stairs, "and watch out for the mess on the floor!"

There was a very excited **WOOF!** from downstairs.

"Oh no!" Lottie groaned. "Einstein's got back in!"

For a second everything fell silent. All that could be heard was the sound of the key in the front door.

"I'm back!" Mum called. The door to the living room clicked open. "Where is everyone?" There was a pause. "And why are there corn flakes all over the living room???"

"Er . . ." Lottie began, but Mum already had a foot on the stairs.

"Why does it look as if it's rained on the staircase?" she asked, following the drips up the stairs.

She opened the door to her bedroom. "What happened here?" Mum gasped. "Have we been burgled? What have you done with Mr and Mrs Good?"

There was a loud **MEOW** followed by a volley of barks. **WOOF! WOOF! WOOF!**

A very damp cat shot up the stairs and headed for Mum's bedroom, followed closely by Mr and Mrs Good.

Al, Lottie, Mia and Filip raced into the room after them.

"Mumsy's got you, Precious!" Mrs Good panted, scooping up her wet pet.

Einstein hurtled in, leaving a trail of orangey-yellow paw prints across the carpet.

He stopped on the heap of clothes in the middle of the room and looked round, puzzled. Mud was dripping off his ears.

"Look out!" Lottie shrieked. "He's going to . . ."

Mrs Good turned and fled as the muck on Einstein's fur splattered everywhere.

"He's rolled in mud and paddled in pee," Lottie groaned. "This is when we really need a time machine. You have to keep on working on it, Al!"

"Of course I do," whispered Al. "Scientists **NEVER** give up! Plus, now we know how our bodies might react when we travel through Space and time—"

From downstairs, there was a terrible shriek. It was Mrs Good, yelling, **"DOG PEE AND SICK!"**

"I'VE STEPPED IN DOG PEE AND SICK! GET IT OFF ME, HAROLD!!!"

Mum looked at the twins and their friends and gave a deep sigh. "I think you need to start explaining," she said, as they all rushed downstairs.

"Yep, we definitely need that time machine," Lottie puffed.

Al patted his notebook. "I'm working on it!" he said.

EARDRUM EXPERIMENT

To show how the eardrum* works

What you will need:

A large bowl

Plastic clingfilm

20–30 grains of uncooked rice

A saucepan and a spoon

How to do the experiment:

Make a giant eardrum
by stretching the plastic
clingfilm over the bowl.
Make sure it is taut.

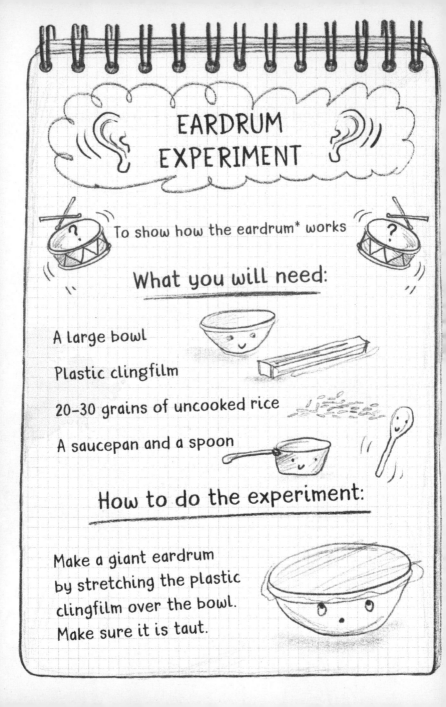

Place the grains of rice on the top of the clingfilm. Make some noise by holding the saucepan and whacking it with the spoon.

Results:

The rice grains jump at the noise. The louder the noise, the higher they jump.

Observations:

1. Hitting the saucepan creates sound waves that make the bowl 'eardrum' vibrate.

2. When our eardrums vibrate, messages get sent to our brain about what we can hear.*

3. The louder the noise, the bigger the vibrations.

4. Mrs Good's shouts make everyone's eardrums vibrate – A LOT!

*Check out the diagram on page 10

TWO EYES EXPERIMENT

To show that two eyes are better than one.

What you will need:

Your eyes and hands

Two pencils

How to do the experiment:

Hold the pencils out flat, at arm's length away from you. Close one eye and try and touch the pencils together.

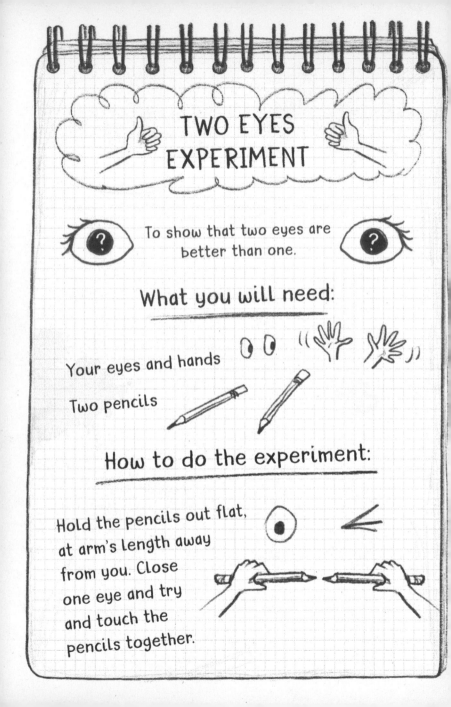

Then do the same thing
with both eyes open.

Results:

It is easy to touch the ends of
the pencils together when
you have both eyes open.

It is more difficult
with one eye shut.

Observations:

1. Two eyes are best for working out how far
away things are.

2. So it's best to keep both eyes open when
you're operating a time machine.

3. Especially if you land in the
past and have to tiptoe
past a T-Rex.

BY JANE CLARKE   ILLUSTRATED BY JAMES BROWN

AL'S AWESOME SCIENCE
Blast-off!

It's the twins' birthday and Al and his friends are experimenting to find out how to blast off his time machine. Trouble is, home-made rockets are difficult to control and messy!

BY JANE CLARKE   ILLUSTRATED BY JAMES BROWN

AL'S AWESOME SCIENCE
Splash Down!

Al is experimenting to find the right covering to help his time-machine capsule survive its splash down back to Earth. But borrowing Mum's bucket and his neighbour's knickers gets him into a real mess!

Read all of my adventures and have fun doing real science experiments at home!

BY JANE CLARKE   ILLUSTRATED BY JAMES BROWN

AL'S AWESOME SCIENCE
Egg-speriments!

Al is experimenting to find the best shape for his time-machine capsule — with Mum's eggs! A nosy neighbour and naughty dog get him into even more trouble!

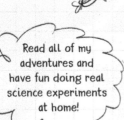